CGP

Maths Activity Book

for ages 9-10

This CGP book is bursting with fun activities to build up children's skills and confidence.

It's ideal for extra practice to reinforce what they're learning in primary school. Enjoy!

Published by CGP

Editors:
Emma Cleasby, Alex Fairer, Katya Parkes and Hannah Roscoe

With thanks to Gail Renaud and Glenn Rogers for the proofreading.

With thanks to Lottie Edwards for the copyright research.

ISBN: 978 1 78908 736 9

Printed by Elanders Ltd, Newcastle upon Tyne.
Clipart on the cover and throughout the book from Corel®
Cover design concept by emc design ltd.

Contents

Working with Numbers

How It Works

When dealing with big numbers, make sure you know the value of each digit.

millions — hundred thousands — ten thousands — thousands — hundreds — tens — ones

6 439 752

You can count forwards and backwards between positive and negative numbers. You may find it helpful to use a number line to do this.

To get from 2 to –5, you need to count back 7 places.

–5   0   5

To get from –1 to 5, you need to count forward 6 places.

Powers of 10 are numbers that are a 10 followed by just zeros. Counting on in powers of 10 just means adding on 10, 100 or another power of 10 each time. Here's an example:

275 521 → 275 621 → 275 721

If you're counting on in steps of 100, find the hundreds digit and add 1 each time.

Now Try These

1. What is the value of the underlined digit in these numbers? Circle your answer.

   1 864 927   8 thousands   8 ten thousands   8 hundred thousands

   7 352 718   5 hundreds   5 thousands   5 ten thousands

2. The table below shows the populations of different cities.
   Fill in the gaps in the sentences below.

Hadwell	Toptown	Mayborne	Peterham	Wolfbury
547 821	875 934	582 301	872 672	575 284

   a) The city of .... has the largest population.

   b) Wolfbury has a larger population than ....

3. 451 092 rabbits live on Thumper island.
   Round this number to the nearest 1000, 10 000 and 100 000.

Nearest 1000

Nearest 10 000

Nearest 100 000

4. Count in steps of 1000 to find the missing numbers in the sequence.

18 479

23 479

5. Martina has a thermometer in her greenhouse. The temperature on Tuesday
   night was −4 degrees. Martina tracks the temperature in the greenhouse
   for the next two days. Fill in the gaps in each of Martina's notes.

Wednesday morning	Wednesday evening	Thursday morning
Temperature: 5 degrees	Temperature: −1 degrees	Temperature: −5 degrees
The temperature is .... degrees higher than on Tuesday night.	The temperature is .... degrees lower than on Wednesday morning.	The temperature is .... degrees lower than on Wednesday evening.

An Extra Challenge

In Bruce's garden, the temperature is −2 °C. He asks his friends who live in different
countries how much colder or warmer it is where they are. Can you work out what the
temperature is for each of Bruce's friends, then match them to the country they live in?

Alim	Helga	Jonas	Dimitri	Helena
13 degrees warmer	5 degrees colder	2 degrees warmer	9 degrees colder	17 degrees warmer

123 News Weather Report

Sweden	India	Germany	Mexico	Russia
−7 °C	15 °C	0 °C	11 °C	−11 °C

How did that go? Did you work
well with these numbers?

Decimals

Decimals are used to show the parts of numbers that are smaller than 1.

Here's an example: 4.572 =

Ones		Tenths	Hundredths	Thousandths
4	.	5	7	2

Here's how to round decimals to one decimal place:

Ones		Tenths	Hundredths
6.86 = 6	.	8	6

To round to one decimal place (tenths), look at the digit to the right of that — the hundredths digit. 6.86 is between 6.8 and 6.9. 6 is the decider, so round up to 6.9.

If the decider is 5 or more, round up. If it is less than 5, round down.

Here's how to round decimals to a whole number:

Ones		Tenths	Hundredths
3.45 = 3	.	4	5

To round to a whole number, look at the digit in the tenths column. 3.45 is between 3 and 4. 4 is the decider, so round down to 3.

1. Write the value of each underlined digit in words. One has been done for you.

   7.54<u>7</u>   .....seven thousandths.....   4.<u>9</u>14   ....

   9.12<u>6</u>   ....   6.8<u>2</u>6   ....

2. Flo is timing how many seconds it takes her dog Zeus to find a treat. Can you write down Zeus's slowest and quickest times?

   7.3   7.329   7.33

         7.036   7.03

   Slowest: [   ]

   Quickest: [   ]

3. Leo's dog has given birth to puppies. Leo weighs each puppy. Write the puppies' names in order from lightest to heaviest.

Roly	Benji	Eddie	Jake	Coco
0.285 kg	0.28 kg	0.209 kg	0.2 kg	0.21 kg

   ....

4. Noelle wants to change the price of some goods in her shop so they're rounded to the nearest 10p. Fill in the price tags by rounding the prices in green to the nearest 10p.

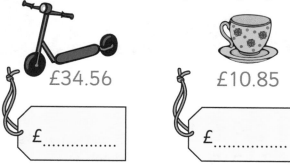

£34.56

£ ....

£10.85

£ ....

£9.33

£ ....

£62.47

£ ....

5. Circle all the numbers that round to 5.

5.93   4.64   5.05   4.48

5.49   4.82   5.50   5.12

6. A group of friends have a running race. Their times in seconds are in the table below. Complete the table by rounding their times to the nearest second.

Anna	Ben	Sharif	Louise	Mia
31.57	36.21	33.72	40.64	38.49
....	....	....	....	....

An Extra Challenge

Sharon has been for a walk every day this week. The distance she walks each day is in the box on the left. Sharon talks about her walks below, but not everything she says is right. Can you spot any mistakes she has made and work out what she should have said?

Monday — 3.179 miles
Tuesday — 3.24 miles
Wednesday — 3.19 miles
Thursday — 3.25 miles
Friday — 3.247 miles
Saturday — 3.17 miles
Sunday — 3.195 miles

My longest walk was on Thursday.

My walk on Friday was longer than my walk on Tuesday.

Thursday's walk rounded to the nearest mile was 3 miles.

My walk on Wednesday was shorter than my walk on Sunday.

My shortest walk was on Monday.

Tuesday's walk rounded to one decimal place was 3.2 miles.

How did these pages go?
Round to the nearest face.

Addition

How It Works

When you're adding big numbers, it's handy to write the sum in columns.

Here's an example: 29 617 + 52 232 = ?

Line up the numbers in place value columns, then add the numbers in each column.

If the answer is more than 9, carry the left-hand digit to the next column, e.g. 9 + 2 = 11.

```
  2 9 6 1 7
+ 5 2 2 3 2
-----------
  8 1 8 4 9
        1
```

This method works for decimals too — just make sure that the decimal points line up.

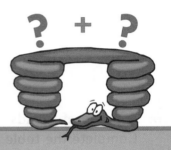

You can use rounding to check whether your answer is sensible.

Round each number to the nearest thousand.

29 617 + 52 232 = ?
30 000 + 52 000 = 82 000

Now Try These

1. Use the column method to answer these additions.

```
  3 6 4 9 3
+ 2 9 4 0 6
```

```
  4 7 0 5 5
+ 3 7 8 6 2
```

```
  7 4 2 6 3 8
+   5 6 8 6 1
```

```
  1 7 . 4 6
+ 5 8 . 3 2
```

```
  6 5 . 4 1
+ 3 2 . 9 7
```

```
  1 6 1 8 0 9
+ 8 3 5 7 9 0
```

```
  2 6 4 9 3 5
+ 6 6 2 5 6 1
```

2. Rumi works at the local balloon factory. On Monday, she made 45 256 balloons, and on Tuesday she made 127 192. How many balloons did she make in total? Use the column method.

+

3. Fill in the missing numbers in the calculations below.

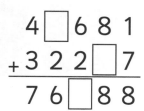
```
  4 □ 6 8 1
+ 3 2 2 □ 7
───────────
  7 6 □ 8 8
```

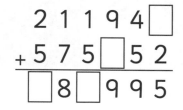
```
  2 1 1 9 4 □
+ 5 7 5 □ 5 2
─────────────
  □ 8 □ 9 9 5
```

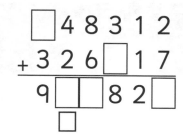
```
  □ 4 8 3 1 2
+ 3 2 6 □ 1 7
─────────────
  9 □ □ 8 2 □
  □
```

4. In the annual snail race, Sid travelled a distance of 25.6 cm. Samba travelled 32.47 cm. How far did the snails travel in total? Use the column method.

+

cm

5. Fatin and Max added together the points they scored on each level of a video game. Use rounding to check their answers, then circle the sum that Fatin and Max got wrong. Write the calculations you used to check the sums on the lines.

14 925 + 21 642 = 36 567 ⟶ ....

81 406 + 86 511 = 157 917 ⟶ ....

103 352 + 97 889 = 201 241 ⟶ ....

An Extra Challenge

In his diary, King Addalot recorded how many people visited his castle. Can you work out how many people visited the castle each year?

In 1654, I welcomed 643 927 guests to my castle.
In 1655, I held lots of fabulous parties — 55 821 more people visited than the year before.
Then in 1656, I hosted an archery competition, so I had 209 236 more visitors than in 1655!
In 1657, 71 015 more people came than the year before, to see the dragon that guards the dungeon.

Are these pages all adding up for you? Put a tick in a box.

Subtraction

How It Works

Using columns makes doing subtractions much simpler.

Here's an example: 846 379 – 320 961 = ?

Line up the numbers in place value columns, then subtract the numbers in each column.

For decimals, remember to line up the decimal points.

```
      5 13
  8 4 6̶ 3̶ 7 9
– 3 2 0 9 6 1
  5 2 5 4 1 8
```

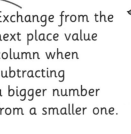

Exchange from the next place value column when subtracting a bigger number from a smaller one.

Rounding is handy for checking your answers to subtractions.

Round each number to the nearest thousand.

846 379 – 320 961 = ?
846 000 – 321 000 = 525 000

Now Try These

1. Use the column method to answer these subtractions.

```
  5 8 6 9 8        6 6 7 2 5        4 6 7 8 9 4
– 3 1 2 7 4      – 5 1 0 2 4      – 2 4 2 9 3 1
```

```
  9 3 7 8 6 1       8 4 . 3 6        7 2 . 6 8       6 4 1 3 0 4
–   2 4 5 8 1     – 5 2 . 7 1      – 4 9 . 6 4     – 2 0 8 1 7 2
```

2. Zara had £78.95 in her purse. At the weekend, she spent £44.49 on a new fish tank. How much money does she have left? Use the column method.

£ _____

3. a) Mr Halbibi's Magic Shop had 847 612 spell books in stock at the start of last year. Over the year, they sold 315 240 books. How many did they have at the end of the year?

b) The magic shop sold 16 154 spell books in a New Year's Day sale. How many books are left?

4. Jude's team ate 64.32 litres of custard in the village custard-eating contest. Keisha's team ate 45.28 litres. How much more custard did Jude's team eat than Keisha's?

5. a) Minuston Jewel Museum has 534 783 diamonds in its collection. They want to sell 42 912 of their diamonds, and calculate that they'll have 482 671 left. Use rounding to check their answer. Write down your calculation below.

....

b) How can you tell that their calculation wasn't right?

....

An Extra Challenge

A famous director is comparing how many people went to see her films on their opening weekends. Can you work out how many people watched Goblins Forever?

947 260 people went to see Captain Wonderful.
461 028 people watched Return of the Mouse.

The difference between them is 91 120 more than the number of people that watched Goblins Forever.

Have you taken away all the information from these pages?

Factors and Multiples

How It Works

A **multiple** of a number is what you get when you multiply that number by another whole number.

$5 \times 7 = 35$ ← So 35 is a multiple of both 5 and 7.

A **factor** of a number is another whole number that divides it exactly. Factors can be written as **factor pairs**.

$35 \div 7 = 5$
and
$35 \div 5 = 7$

$5 \times 7 = 35$, so 5 and 7 are a factor pair of 35.

If two numbers have the same factor, it's called a **common factor**.

$35 \div 5 = 7$ and $40 \div 5 = 8$

So 5 is a common factor of 35 and 40.

A **prime number** is a number that can only be divided by itself and 1.

5 ← The factors of 5 are 1 and 5 only, so it's a prime number.

Now Try These

1. Which statements are right? Put a tick (✔) or a cross (✘) next to each one.

   a) 24 is a multiple of 4. ☐

   b) 6 is a factor of 32. ☐

   c) 41 is a multiple of 3. ☐

   d) 9 is a factor of 54. ☐

2. Each cake below has a different number of cherries on it.
   Circle all the cakes which have a prime number of cherries.

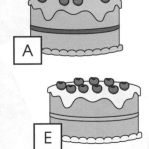
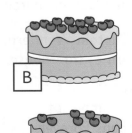
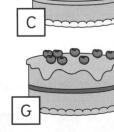
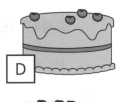
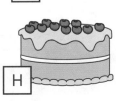

3. Imran wrote the factor pairs of 56 on this board.

   a) Some of the numbers were rubbed off the board. Write the missing factors in the boxes to complete each factor pair.

   b) Now write down the factor pairs of 63.

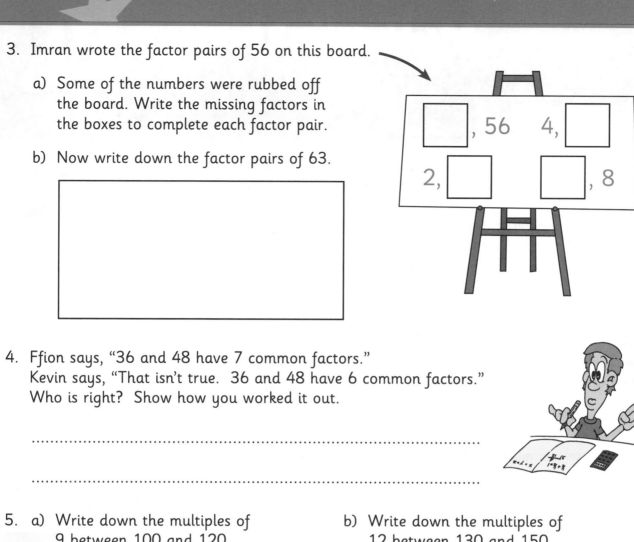

☐ , 56   4, ☐

2, ☐   ☐ , 8

4. Ffion says, "36 and 48 have 7 common factors."
   Kevin says, "That isn't true. 36 and 48 have 6 common factors."
   Who is right? Show how you worked it out.

   ....

   ....

5. a) Write down the multiples of 9 between 100 and 120.

      ....

   b) Write down the multiples of 12 between 130 and 150.

      ....

   c) Write down the multiples of 6 between 80 and 100.

      ....

   d) Write down the multiples of 7 between 90 and 110.

      ....

An Extra Challenge

You're in the final round of a game show. To win a prize, you need to find the right numbers in the grid.

a) Which numbers are prime numbers?

b) Three of the numbers share the same two common factors. Which numbers are they and what are the common factors?

WIN A PRIZE!

47	81	57
64	45	59
29	52	31

Were you in your prime while working through these pages?

 ☐   ☐   ☐

Multiplication

How It Works

You can multiply by 10, 100 and even 1000 in your head by thinking about place value. Here's an example: $2.7 \times 100 = ?$

100 has two zeros, so you need to move each digit 2 places to the left. →

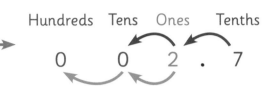

Hundreds Tens Ones Tenths

$$0 \quad 0 \quad 2 \ . \ 7$$

So the answer is 270.

Multiplying a 4-digit number by one digit can be done using columns. Here's an example: $1285 \times 4 = ?$

```
  T H T O
  1 2 8 5
×       4
  5 1 4 0
  1 3 2
```

Line up the numbers according to their place value.

You can use a similar method to multiply 3-digit and 4-digit numbers by a 2-digit number. Here's an example: $1285 \times 21 = ?$

First, find 1285×1... →

...and then find 1285×20. →

Add them together for the answer. →

```
      1 2 8 5
  ×      2 1
      1 2 8 5
    2 5 7 0 0
        1 1
    2 6 9 8 5
```

Now Try These

1. Complete each multiplication with the right number.

   a) $7.4 \times 10 =$ ....

   b) $15 \times$ .... $= 1500$

   c) .... $\times 82 = 82\ 000$

   d) $100 \times 9.33 =$ ....

2. A scientist needs help calculating the results of an experiment. Help her solve these multiplications so she can finish her work.

   a)
   ```
        1280
   ×       3
   ```

   b)
   ```
        1095
   ×       5
   ```

   c)
   ```
        3412
   ×       6
   ```

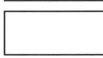

3. What number is:

   a) 60 times bigger than 781?

   b) 14 times bigger than 991?

   c) 41 times bigger than 513?

×
_____

_____

☐

×
_____

_____

☐

×
_____

_____

☐

4. a) Farmer Steve grew 2304 carrots on his farm last year. Farmer Wanda grew 13 times more carrots than Farmer Steve.

How many carrots did Farmer Wanda grow? Show your working.

b) Two rainforests are home to flocks of parrots. The first rainforest has 3653 parrots. The second rainforest has 21 times more parrots.

How many parrots live in the second rainforest? Show your working.

An Extra Challenge

Parts of the answers to the calculations below are missing. Can you work out the missing digits by solving the calculations and matching them up with their answers?

152 × 43   3293 × 30

7481 × 7   4503 × 6

2? 01?   9? ?90

?536   ?2 ?67

Are you a multiplication master? Give a box a tick.

 ☐   ☐   ☐

Division

How It Works

To divide a number by 10, 100 and 1000, move the digits to the right. Here's an example: 450 ÷ 1000 = ?

1000 has three zeros, so you need to move each digit 3 places to the right.

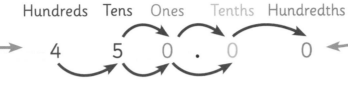

| Hundreds | Tens | Ones | Tenths | Hundredths |

4 5 0 . 0 0

Remove any zeros after the last digit.

So the answer is **0.45**.

You can use short division to divide by a 1-digit number. Take the number you want to divide and split it into thousands, hundreds, tens and ones. Then divide each number individually.

Here's an example: 3129 ÷ 3 = ?

```
    1 0 4 3
3 | 3 1 ¹2 9
```

1 hundred can't be divided by 3 to give any hundreds. So exchange the 1 hundred for 10 tens.

When a number can't be divided exactly by another number, there will be a remainder.

```
    0 3 5 1  r 3
5 | 1 ¹7 ²5 8
```

You can write remainders as **numbers**, **fractions** or **decimals**.

351 r 3   351$\frac{3}{5}$ 351.6

Now Try These

1. Solve these calculations.

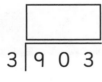

3 | 9 0 3

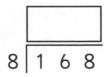

8 | 1 6 8

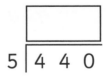

5 | 4 4 0

2. Draw lines to match each calculation to its missing number.
    One has been done for you.

68 ÷ ? = 6.8   10   386 ÷ ? = 3.86

2190 ÷ ? = 219 —— 100   702 ÷ ? = 0.702

4.3 ÷ ? = 0.43   1000   15.5 ÷ ? = 0.155

3. A factory made 4776 baubles. Each of the 4 people working in the factory made the same number of baubles. How many did each person make?

Each person made .... baubles.

4. Tiana divides 7326 by 6. She divides the answer by 100. What is the final number?

The final number is:

5. a) 4 dolphins are hunting when they find a shoal of 1459 fish. They share the fish evenly and eat as many whole fish as they can.

Work out how many fish each dolphin eats and how many are left over.

b) 3 more dolphins join the 4 dolphins on their next hunt. This time, they find 5353 fish and they share the fish out evenly again.

How many fish does each dolphin eat now?

.... fish

.... left over

.... fish

.... left over

An Extra Challenge

Can you work out the answer to each of Graeme's questions?

I'm thinking of a number. I multiply it by 10, then I multiply the new number by 8. My answer is 1672. What was the original number?

If I divide 2469 by 5, what will the remainder be?

True or false? The answer to 4676 divided by 7 is the same as 6012 divided by 9.

Did these calculations get your undivided attention?

15

Fractions 1

How It Works

When two fractions show the same amount, they are called **equivalent fractions**.

$\frac{1}{3}$ →

$\frac{2}{6}$ →

Each shape has been split into a different number of segments, but the same amount has been shaded.

This means $\frac{1}{3}$ and $\frac{2}{6}$ are equivalent fractions.

Percentages tell you an amount out of 100. They're written with a per cent (%) symbol.

This is how you write a percentage as a **fraction**:

$10\% \rightarrow \frac{10}{100}$

Put the percentage on the top...

...and 100 on the bottom.

You can also write **decimals** as fractions. All you need to do is look at the tenths, hundredths and thousandths. Here's an example:

Tenths Hundredths Thousandths

0 . 6   2   4

This decimal is 6 tenths, 2 hundredths and 4 thousandths, which is the same as 624 thousandths. So it's equivalent to $\frac{624}{1000}$.

Improper fractions and **mixed numbers** are two ways to write fractions greater than 1. Here's an example:

$\frac{7}{5}$ ← In improper fractions, the top number is always larger than the bottom number.

$1\frac{2}{5}$ ← Mixed numbers are written with whole numbers and fractions.

Now Try These

1. A bag contains 100 marbles. Quentin takes 10, Sofia takes 30 and Bogdan takes 60. Write these numbers down as tenths.

    Quentin ⟶ $\frac{\boxed{}}{10}$ Sofia ⟶ $\frac{\boxed{}}{10}$ Bogdan ⟶ $\frac{\boxed{}}{10}$

2. Fill in the gaps with the right numbers to show these values as fractions.

    $37\% = \frac{\boxed{}}{100}$ $0.86 = \frac{86}{\boxed{}}$ $54\% = \frac{\boxed{}}{100}$ $0.102 = \frac{102}{\boxed{}}$

3. Shade the second and third shapes so that the amount shaded is equivalent to the first. Then fill in the boxes to show the equivalent fractions.

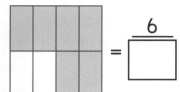 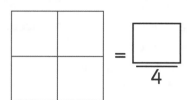 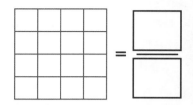

4. An ice cream seller is calculating how many tubs of ice cream they have left. They write down a fraction for each flavour. Rewrite the fractions as mixed numbers.

vanilla **strawberry** **bubblegum** **chocolate**

$\frac{9}{5} = $ ☐ $\frac{5}{3} = $ ☐ $\frac{27}{11} = $ ☐ $\frac{19}{8} = $ ☐

5. Cross out the improper fractions that are wrong, then rewrite them so they are right.

$2\frac{2}{3} = \frac{8}{3}$ $3\frac{1}{2} = \frac{9}{2}$ $7\frac{4}{5} = \frac{33}{5}$

   $4\frac{2}{6} = \frac{24}{6}$ $5\frac{3}{4} = \frac{23}{4}$

An Extra Challenge

Briony is trapped in a witch's lair. To escape, she needs to unlock a secret door. The door's lock has three groups of fractions on it. Briony needs to find the fraction in each group that isn't equivalent to the others. Can you help her find the right fractions?

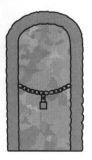

$\frac{4}{6}$	$\frac{12}{18}$
$\frac{20}{30}$	$\frac{1}{3}$

$\frac{3}{4}$	$\frac{16}{24}$
$\frac{12}{16}$	$\frac{6}{8}$

$\frac{5}{21}$	$\frac{10}{35}$
$\frac{2}{7}$	$\frac{20}{70}$

Can you think of one equivalent fraction for each fraction you've helped Briony to find?

Are you a confident fraction finder after these questions?

 ☐   ☐   ☐

Diving the Depths

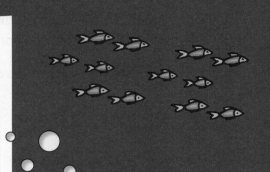

Xin and her team have been exploring the ocean depths in a submarine. They have a logbook to record data for their research. Can you help them complete each page by filling in the missing information? Xin highlighted some key digits — keep an eye out for them as you go.

1 — SUBMARINE DEPTH MEASUREMENTS

Depth (feet)	Rounded figure (nearest 1000)
11 820	
15 468	
19 157	
23 913	
27 176	

2 — WATER TEMPERATURE

At 0 m, it's 23 °C. It drops by 2 °C every 500 m until −3500 m — it stays the same below that.

At −250 m, the water temperature is .... °C

At −2000 m, the water temperature is .... °C

At −3500 m, the water temperature is .... °C

3 — JELLYFISH SIGHTINGS

Three fifths of the jellyfish glowed in the dark. This means that .... % of the jellyfish didn't glow in the dark.

The first swarm had 25 jellyfish, the second swarm had 40 jellyfish and the third swarm had 18 jellyfish. Was the total number of jellyfish a prime number?

YES ☐   NO ☐

4 — SEAWATER SAMPLES

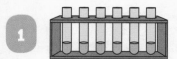

1 Six samples.
Each one is
1296 ml.

Total amount:

.... ml

2 Three samples.
Each one is
5475 ml.

Total amount:

.... ml

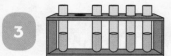

3 Five samples.
Each one is
2803 ml.

Total amount:

.... ml

5 — DISTANCE MEASUREMENTS

The ocean trench we explored was 9.3 km deep.

This is .... m .

We dived to a depth of 8700 m. We travelled 1400 m

forward, then travelled back up to the surface.

We travelled .... km in total.

6 — THE NEXT DIVE

To reveal the secret directions, put the highlighted digits
into the gaps in the order they appear in the logbook.

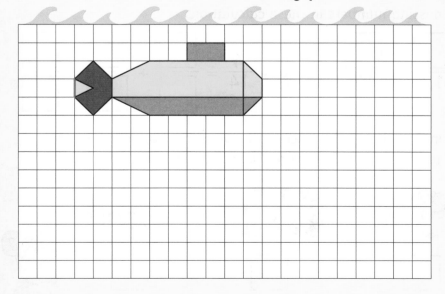

■ RIGHT, ■ DOWN

to reach Point A

CHANGE DIRECTION
(REFLECT SIDEWAYS
ACROSS THE RED LINE)

then

■ LEFT, ■ DOWN

to reach Point B

Draw the submarine's
position at point A
and at point B.

Fractions 2

How It Works

To order fractions when all the denominators (bottom numbers) are the same, compare the numerators (top numbers). If the denominators are different, find equivalent fractions.

$$\frac{3}{4} \qquad \frac{7}{8} \qquad \frac{13}{16} \qquad \frac{1}{2}$$

First, you need to find a common denominator. In this example, you can multiply to find equivalent fractions with denominators of 16.

$$\frac{3}{4} = \frac{12}{16} \qquad \frac{7}{8} = \frac{14}{16} \qquad \frac{1}{2} = \frac{8}{16}$$

So from smallest to largest:

$$\frac{1}{2} \qquad \frac{3}{4} \qquad \frac{13}{16} \qquad \frac{7}{8}$$

To add and subtract fractions, the denominators must be the same.
You'll need to find equivalent fractions if the denominators are different.

$$\frac{2}{5} + \frac{3}{10} = \textbf{?} \longrightarrow \frac{2}{5} = \frac{4}{10} \longrightarrow \frac{4}{10} + \frac{3}{10} = \frac{7}{10}$$

Multiplying a whole number by a fraction is the same as finding the fraction of the amount. You need to multiply by the numerator and divide by the denominator. For mixed numbers, multiply the whole number and fraction parts separately, then add the answers together.

$$\frac{1}{3} \times 8 = \textbf{?} \longrightarrow \frac{1}{3} \times 8 = \frac{1 \times 8}{3} = \frac{8}{3} = 2\frac{2}{3}$$

8 divided by 3 doesn't give a whole number, so just multiply the numerator by 8 instead.

Now Try These

1. Fill in the boxes with the missing numbers in these calculations.

$$\frac{7}{12} - \frac{2}{6} = \frac{\boxed{}}{12} - \frac{\boxed{}}{12} = \frac{\boxed{}}{12} \qquad \frac{1}{2} + \frac{4}{14} = \frac{\boxed{}}{\boxed{}} + \frac{\boxed{}}{\boxed{}} = \frac{\boxed{}}{\boxed{}}$$

2. A mouse eats some food in a kitchen. The fractions below show how much of each food is left. Number the fractions from 1-4, with 1 being the smallest fraction.

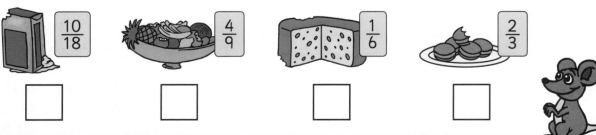

$$\frac{10}{18} \qquad\qquad \frac{4}{9} \qquad\qquad \frac{1}{6} \qquad\qquad \frac{2}{3}$$

3. Use the diagrams to help you do these multiplications.
   If the answer is more than 1, write it as a mixed number.

   a) $\frac{1}{7} \times 4 =$ ....

   b) $\frac{3}{5} \times 3 =$ ....

   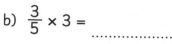 

   c) $\frac{2}{6} \times 5 =$ ....

   d) $\frac{5}{8} \times 2 =$ ....

4. a) Natalia is trying to crack the code on a safe. First, she needs to solve the
      calculations below. Help her work out what the missing digits are.

   $$1\frac{5}{12} - \frac{8}{12} = \frac{\square}{12} - \frac{\square}{12} = \frac{\square}{12} \qquad \frac{1}{3} + \frac{3}{24} = \frac{\square}{24} + \frac{\square}{24} = \frac{\square}{24}$$

   $$\frac{4}{16} + \frac{5}{8} = \frac{\square}{\square} + \frac{\square}{\square} = \frac{\square}{8} \qquad \frac{13}{6} - 1\frac{1}{3} = \frac{\square}{\square} - \frac{\square}{\square} = \frac{\square}{6}$$

   b) Now help Natalia put the answers in order,
      starting with the largest fraction.

   largest   smallest

An Extra Challenge

A farmer collects wool from a herd of 12 alpacas. Can you
work out how many bags of wool the farmer collects in total?

- 3 of the alpacas produce $\frac{4}{5}$ bags of wool each.

- 4 of the alpacas produce $1\frac{1}{10}$ bags of wool each.

- 5 of the alpacas produce $1\frac{6}{15}$ bags of wool each.

How confident do you feel after
this second helping of fractions?

21

Converting Units

How It Works

To convert between different **metric units**, you need to know how they're equivalent to each other.

> 1 kilometre (km) = 1000 metres (m)
> 1 metre (m) = 100 centimetres (cm)
> 1 centimetre (cm) = 10 millimetres (mm)
> 1 kilogram (kg) = 1000 grams (g)
> 1 litre (l) = 1000 millilitres (ml)

Example: Convert 3.6 m into centimetres.

1 m = 100 cm
3.6 × 100 = 360
So 3.6 m = **360 cm**

You can convert metric units into **imperial units** using these common conversions:

> 8 kilometres (km) ≈ 5 miles
> 1 metre (m) ≈ 3 feet
> 5 centimetres (cm) ≈ 2 inches
> 1 kilogram (kg) ≈ 2 pounds
> 100 grams (g) ≈ 4 ounces
> 1 litre (l) ≈ 2 pints

← These aren't exact, but they're close enough for you to use them in rough calculations.

Example: Convert 300 g into ounces.

100 g ≈ 4 ounces
300 g is 3 lots of 100 g
So 300 g ≈ 3 × 4 ounces = **12 ounces**

This symbol means 'approximately equal to'.

Some problems could involve converting measurements of time. Here's an example:

It takes 2 hours for a runner to complete a race. What is this time in minutes? ⟶ There are 60 minutes in an hour.
2 × 60 = **120 minutes**

Now Try These

1. Which statements are right? Put a tick (✔) or a cross (✗) next to each one.

   a) 9 metres ≈ 24 feet ☐

   b) 15 centimetres ≈ 6 inches ☐

   c) 16 kilometres ≈ 10 miles ☐

   d) 7 kilograms ≈ 12 pounds ☐

2. Sydney the snake wants to convert some measurements, but he can't remember how to do it. Draw lines to match each conversion to the right method. One has been done for you.

mm to m	kg to g	cm to mm	ml to l	cm to m

| × 10 | ÷ 1000 | ÷ 100 | × 1000 | ÷ 1000 |

3. The Patel family are competing to see who can complete a jigsaw puzzle in the quickest time. Sonal finishes her puzzle in 2 days, 6 hours and 37 minutes. Whose times in the table below did she beat?

Family member	Time
Mum	53 hours 42 minutes
Dad	55 hours 26 minutes
Brother	54 hours 47 minutes
Grandpa	54 hours 18 minutes

....

4. Fill in the missing values and units in these conversions.

a) 4210 g = ... kg

b) 15.5 litres = ... ml

c) 3860 m = 3.86 ....

d) 17 cm = ... m

e) 2290 .... = 2.29 m

f) 10.52 .... = 10 520 g

5. Marek spends 52 weeks travelling around the world. He spends 98 days in South America, 15 weeks in Asia, 63 days in Africa, and then he spends the remaining weeks in Europe. Where did he spend the most time?

Marek spent the most time in ....

An Extra Challenge

A chef wants to make a top secret tomato pasta recipe at their restaurant. They've managed to find the ingredients list below, but the measurements aren't written in sensible units.

a) Can you convert these amounts into more sensible units?

2250 g tomatoes
1500 ml chicken stock
0.52 kg pasta
0.05 l olive oil
0.03 kg fresh herbs

b) This list shows how much of each ingredient the chef has. Can they make the tomato pasta?

5 pounds tomatoes
3 pints chicken stock
12 ounces pasta
1 pint olive oil
2 ounces fresh herbs

Did your maths skills measure up on these pages?

Problem Solving

How It Works

Some problems won't tell you what methods to use, so you'll have to decide what to do. Here's an example:

A captain has 480 cm of rope. They use half of it to tie up the sails, then they use one quarter of the remaining rope to secure the anchor. How much rope is used in total?

Start by finding one half of 480 cm. ➡ 480 ÷ 2 = 240 cm ⬅ Add these two amounts together to get the final answer.

Now divide this by 4 to find one quarter. ➡ 240 ÷ 4 = 60 cm ⬅

= **300 cm**

You might need to convert fractions into **percentages** or **decimals** when solving problems:

$\frac{1}{2}$ ➡ 50% ➡ 0.5 $\frac{1}{5}$ ➡ 20% ➡ 0.2 $\frac{1}{10}$ ➡ 10% ➡ 0.1

$\frac{1}{4}$ ➡ 25% ➡ 0.25 $\frac{2}{5}$ ➡ 40% ➡ 0.4

$\frac{3}{4}$ ➡ 75% ➡ 0.75 $\frac{4}{5}$ ➡ 80% ➡ 0.8

Take a look at these examples of how to convert fractions:

To convert a fraction to a percentage, find an equivalent fraction with a denominator of 100.

$\overset{\times 4}{\frac{8}{25}} \underset{\times 4}{\to} \frac{32}{100} = \mathbf{32\%}$ $\overset{\div 3}{\frac{45}{300}} \underset{\div 3}{\to} \frac{15}{100} = \mathbf{15\%}$

To convert a fraction into a decimal, find the percentage, then divide it by 100.

32 ÷ 100 = **0.32**   15 ÷ 100 = **0.15**

Now Try These

1. Maisie buys three bottles of fizzy pop for her birthday party.

   The guests at her party drink 670 ml of cola, 1280 ml of fizzy cherry and 940 ml of fizzy orange. How much fizzy pop is left in total?

.... ml

2. a) A pasta factory can make 47 packets of spaghetti every minute. Each packet weighs
        325 g. How many kilograms of spaghetti can the factory make every minute?

.... kg

    b) 20% of the pasta is sold to a restaurant and $\frac{1}{2}$ is sold to a supermarket.
        What proportion of pasta is left over? Give your answer as a decimal.

....

3. a) Liam spends £1.50 a week on a magazine subscription
        and half as much a week on trading cards. How much
        money will he have spent after 10 weeks?

£.........................

    b) After the 10 weeks, Liam will have spent $\frac{3}{4}$ of his money on the magazine
        subscription and the trading cards. How much money did he start with?

£.........................

An Extra Challenge

Three friends are taking part in a race around the world.

Sinead travels 1660 km in the first week. In the same week, Jerome
travels 50% of this distance, but Zia travels $\frac{1}{10}$ further than Sinead.

Using this information, can you work out...

  a) ...how far Sinead travels in four weeks if she covers the
      same distance each week as she did in the first week?

  b) ...how far Jerome travels in the first week?

  c) ...how far Zia travels in the first week?

Did you manage to solve these
pesky problems? Tick a box.

Shapes and Angles

How It Works

Angles are measured in degrees (°). They have different names depending on their size:

An **acute** angle is less than 90° (a quarter turn).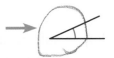

A **right angle** is exactly 90° (one quarter turn).

An **obtuse** angle is more than 90° but less than 180° (between a quarter turn and a half turn).

A **reflex** angle is larger than 180° (between a half turn and one whole turn).

You can estimate the size of an angle by comparing it with one of these:

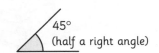 45° (half a right angle) 90° 180° 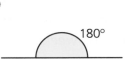 270° 360°

To draw and measure angles accurately, you need to use a protractor.

Regular shapes have sides that are all the same length, and all their angles are the same size. This isn't true for irregular shapes.

regular hexagon 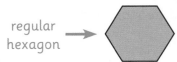 irregular hexagon

Rectangles have two pairs of parallel sides. The sides in each pair are the same length, and each angle is 90°.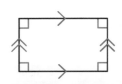

Now Try These

1. Without measuring them, match these angles to the correct size.

A   B   C   D

95°   200°   140°   15°

2. Circle all the regular shapes.

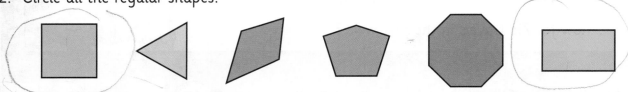

26

3. Karthik has drawn four rectangles. He's added some measurements to each one. Can you calculate the missing values?

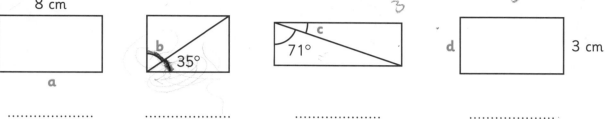

$1 \triangle 2 = 180$ $\quad 3$

$H \boxed{} 2 = 360°$ $\quad 3$

8 cm

b
35°

c
71°

d   3 cm

a

....

4. Use a protractor to measure the first angle, then draw the second angle.

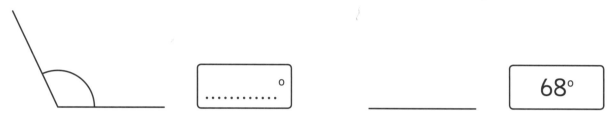

............°

68°

5. Find the missing angle in each of the diagrams below.

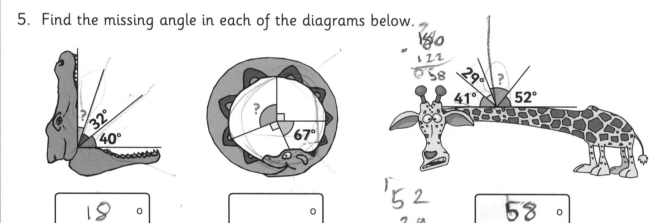

180
122
58

29° ?
41° 52°

32°
40°

?

67°

18 °
....

°
....

5 2
2 9
4 1
1 2 8

58 °
....

An Extra Challenge

A machine is sorting chocolate shapes into three different groups. Some of the chocolates have already been sorted. Where do you think the machine will put the other chocolates?

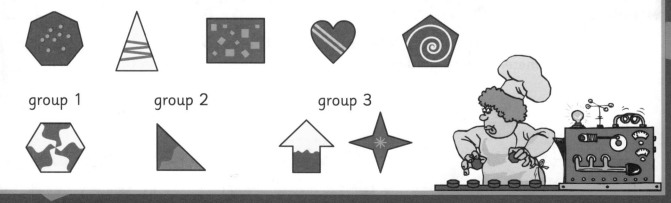

group 1   group 2   group 3

How do you think your angle
skills are shaping up?

 ☐   ☐ ☐   ☐

Perimeter and Area

How It Works

Perimeter is the distance around the outside of a shape. Find it by adding up the lengths of the sides. Some of the lengths might be missing, so you'll have to work these out.

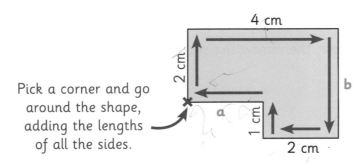

Pick a corner and go around the shape, adding the lengths of all the sides.

The shape is 4 cm wide, so side a is 4 − 2 = 2 cm long.

To find side b, you need to add the purple lengths together: 2 + 1 = 3 cm

So the total perimeter is:
2 + 4 + 3 + 2 + 1 + 2 = **14 cm**

You won't always be told the measurements for a shape, so you might have to use a ruler.

Area is the space inside the shape. You can work it out by counting how many squares are covered on a grid. Sometimes a shape won't fit perfectly inside the squares. You can estimate the shape's area by counting how many squares are more than half filled.

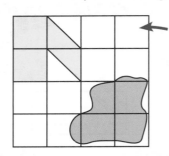

Each square's area is 1 cm^2.

The yellow shape covers two whole squares and two half squares. So its area is $1 + 1 + \frac{1}{2} + \frac{1}{2} = 3$ cm^2.

In the green shape, there are 4 squares that are more than half covered. So its area is about 4 cm^2.

To calculate the area of squares and rectangles, just multiply the width by the length.

Example: A rectangle is 6 cm wide and 8 cm long. What is its area? $6 \times 8 =$ **48 cm^2**

Now Try These

1. A gardener is working in three different gardens. Use the sketches below to work out the perimeter of each garden. Not all of the lengths are given in the sketches.

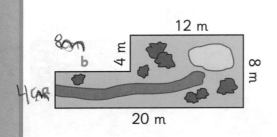

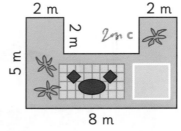

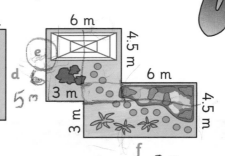

2. What is the area of each of these signs?

1 square = 1 m²

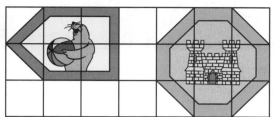

11 cm

7 cm

FOR SALE

9 cm

9 cm

3. Marnie has collected some shells from the beach. Use the grid to estimate the area of each shell.

1 square = 1 cm²

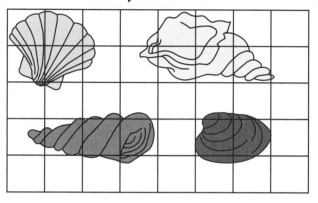

4. Use a ruler to measure the perimeters of the shapes below. Give your answers in cm.

a)

b)

c)

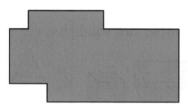

....

5. Work out the missing values for the rectangles described below.

a) Its perimeter is 14 cm and its length is 5 cm. What is its width?

b) Its perimeter is 26 cm and its width is 4 cm. What is its length?

c) Its perimeter is 31 cm and its length is 12 cm. What is its width?

d) Its width is 6.5 cm and its length is 8 cm. What is its perimeter?

An Extra Challenge

Bao is making biscuits for a bake sale. He rolls out some dough and cuts out bear shapes. Can you estimate what area of dough will be left once Bao cuts out all of the bear shapes?

Each grid square has an area of 1 cm².

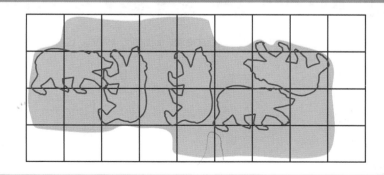

How do you rate your perimeter and area-finding skills?

3D Shapes

Volume is the amount of space a shape takes up. It's measured in cubic units, like cubic centimetres (cm³) or cubic metres (m³). You can find volumes by counting cubes.

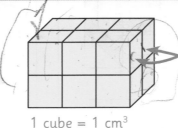

1 cube = 1 cm³

This cuboid is made up of two sets of 6 cubes. So its volume is 2 × 6 = 12 cm³.

Sometimes cubes will be hidden behind other cubes.

Capacity is the amount that something can hold. It's also measured in cubic units.

Example: Find the capacity of the hole in this shape.

The hole in the shape is 4 cubes big, or 4 cm³. This means that the capacity of the hole is 4 cm³.

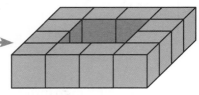

1 cube = 1 cm³

3D shapes are solid shapes. Here are some examples:

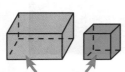

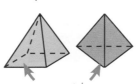
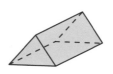

cuboids (cubes are a type of cuboid)   cone   sphere   pyramids   triangular prism   cylinder

They can be represented in different ways:

A **plan** shows you the view from directly above a 3D shape.	A **net** folds up to make a 3D shape.	An **elevation** is the view from one side.
E.g. 	E.g.	E.g.

1. If the volume of 1 cube is 1 cm³, what is the volume of each of the shapes below?

   a)

   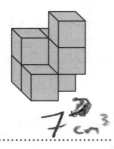

   7 cm³

   ....

   b)

   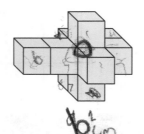

   10 cm

   ....

   c)

   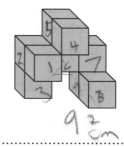

   9 cm

   ....

2. Draw lines to match each net to the 3D shape it makes.

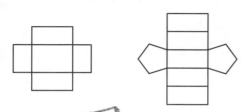

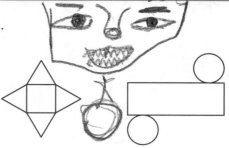

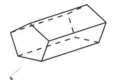

3. a) Owyn makes accessories for toys. He's made the three bags below. What is the capacity of each one? Hint: the bottom layer of each bag has no holes in it.

1 cube = 1 cm³

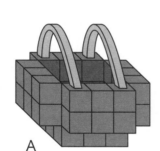

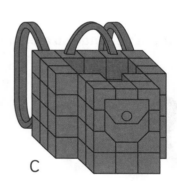

A   B   C

b) If there can't be two of the same item in a bag, what combination of these items would totally fill each bag's capacity? Hint: ignore bits that stick out from the cubes.

1 cube = 1 cm³   keyring

mobile phone

orange

sweet

An Extra Challenge

Rafi shows you this photo of his farm.

Can you draw...

a) ...the plan of the farm buildings?

b) ...the left side elevation of the farm buildings?

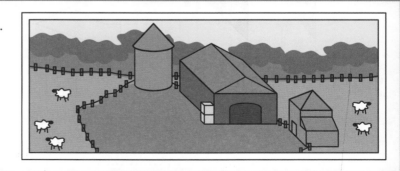

Have you reached your full capacity with 3D shapes?

31

Reflection and Translation

How It Works

You can reflect shapes in a mirror line. Each point and its reflection are exactly the same distance from the mirror line.

Vertical mirror lines reflect shapes sideways.

Horizontal mirror lines reflect shapes upwards or downwards.

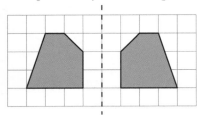

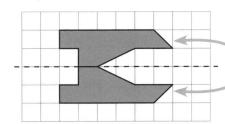

Reflected shapes are the same size and shape as the original shape.

Translation is when you move a shape without rotating or reflecting it. It doesn't change size or shape — just position. Here are some examples:

Translate this shape 5 squares to the right then 3 squares up.

Translate this shape 4 squares to the left then 4 squares down.

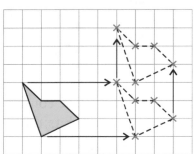

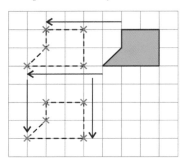

Now Try These

1. a) Tick (✔) or cross (✗) each box to say whether each grid shows a correct translation.

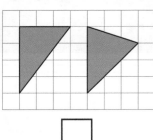

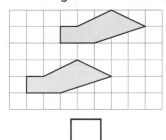

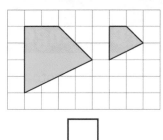

b) If you've crossed any boxes, explain why the translations aren't right.

....

....

2. Carys has drawn a mirror line next to each of these patterns. Shade in squares on the other side of each line to make the patterns symmetrical in the mirror lines.

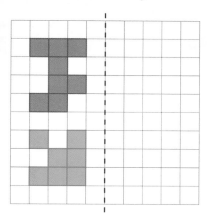 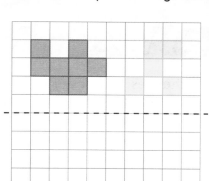 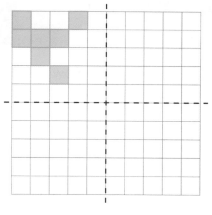

3. Describe how the circles labelled '1' have been translated to give the circles labelled '2'.

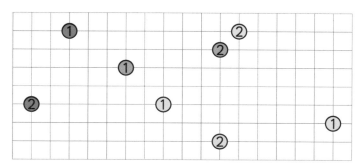

red: ....

orange: ....

blue: ....

yellow: ....

4. Reflect the shape in the mirror line, then translate the reflection using Miss Malkin's instructions.

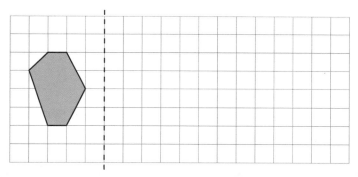

Translate the reflection 7 squares right and 2 squares down. Draw the shape. Translate this new shape 3 squares left and 4 squares up. Draw the shape.

An Extra Challenge

Neil buys a roll of wallpaper with the symmetrical pattern below.
He thinks some parts of the pattern are wrong. Can you find the 5 mistakes?

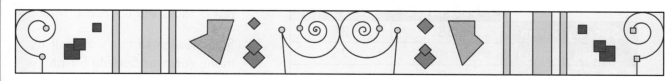

Did you translate your
reflection skills into success?

Graphs and Tables

How It Works

Line graphs show how something changes. You need to be able to solve problems using the data from line graphs. Here's an example:

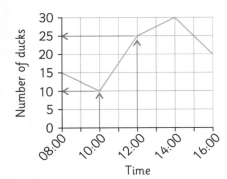

This graph shows how the number of ducks in a park changed over the course of one day.

How many more ducks were there in the park at 12:00 than at 10:00?

There were 10 ducks at 10:00 and there were 25 ducks at 12:00. So there were 25 − 10 = **15 more ducks** at 12:00.

Tables are one way of presenting and organising data. You could be asked to fill in missing data or find specific information in tables. Take a look at this example:

This timetable shows bus times for four different bus stops.

Jade Close	Ruby Meadows	Diamond Lane	Emerald Avenue
12:34	12:49	13:01	13:06
12:58	13:13	13:25	13:30
?	13:37	13:49	13:54

Timetables often use the 24-hour clock.

a) Find the missing time.

You can see from the other rows that Jade Close and Ruby Meadows are 15 minutes apart. So take 15 minutes away from 13:37 to find the missing time ⟶ 13:37 − 15 = **13:22**

b) You miss the 13:25 bus at Diamond Lane. How long do you have to wait for the next one?

Take 25 away from 49 to find the waiting time ⟶ 49 − 25 = **24 minutes**

Now Try These

1. Will owns four racing snails. He records the snails' details in a table. Complete the table using the information below.

	Total races	Total wins
Speedy Susan	38	34
Slimy Shelly		26
Steve T Snail	42	
Sally Slowpoke	29	

- Slimy Shelly has entered 7 fewer races than Steve T Snail.

- Sally Slowpoke has won half as many races as Speedy Susan.

- Steve T Snail's total wins are 13 more than Slimy Shelly's.

2. This graph shows the rainwater collected in a container during a storm. Are the following statements true or false?

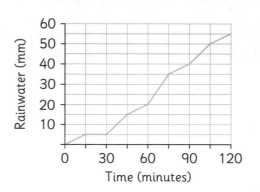

a) 25 mm of rainwater was collected between 45 and 90 minutes.

b) There was 40 mm less rainwater in the container after 60 minutes than there was after 120 minutes.

3. A town is preparing for its annual Christmas parades. The timetable below shows when each parade will reach different parts of the town.

	Church	Library	Museum	Main Square
Parade 1	11:17	11:29	11:42	12:00
Parade 2	15:42	15:56	16:17	16:33
Parade 3	19:38	19:53	20:05	20:25

a) How long will it take for Parade 2 to get from the church to the museum?

....

b) Which parade will last the longest?

....

c) This line graph shows how many people have watched the parades since they began.

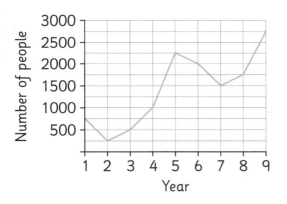

How many fewer people watched the parades in year 3 than in year 8?

....

In year 10, the number of people is halfway between the figures for year 2 and year 5. How many people is this?

....

An Extra Challenge

Can you draw a table that presents all the information from the notes below? Label your columns like this:

Item	Total ordered

fabric squares
5 packs of 68

balls of wool
7 boxes of 36

beads
9 packs of 150

coloured threads
2 boxes of 214

Do you have tip-top table skills after doing these questions?

Answers

Pages 2-3 — Working with Numbers

1. 1 **8**64 927: 8 hundred thousands
   7 **3**52 718: 5 ten thousands
2. a) Toptown   b) Hadwell
3. 451 000   450 000   500 000
4. 18 479   19 479   20 479   21 479   22 479   23 479
5. 9   6   4

An Extra Challenge

Alim: 11 °C (Mexico), Helga: −7 °C (Sweden), Jonas: 0 °C (Germany), Dimitri: −11 °C (Russia), Helena: 15 °C (India)

Pages 4-5 — Decimals

1. 7.54**7**: seven thousandths   4.**9**14: nine tenths
   9.12**6**: six thousandths   6.8**2**6: two hundredths
2. Slowest: 7.33   Quickest: 7.03
3. Jake, Eddie, Coco, Benji, Roly
4. £34.60   £10.90   £9.30   £62.50
5. 4.64   5.05   5.49   4.82   5.12
6.

	Anna	Ben	Sharif	Louise	Mia
	31.57	36.21	33.72	40.64	38.49
	32	36	34	41	38

An Extra Challenge

'My shortest walk was on Monday' should be 'My shortest walk was on Saturday'.

Pages 6-7 — Addition

1.
```
  36493        47055      742638        17.46
+ 29406      + 37862    +  56861      + 58.32
  65899        84917      799499        75.78
      1            1           1            1

  65.41       161809       264935
+ 32.97      +835790      +662561
  98.38       997599       927496
      1            1            1  1
```

2.
```
  127192
+   45256
  172448
      1 1
```

3.
```
  44681       211943       648312
+ 32207      +575052      +326517
  76888       786995       974829
                                 1
```

4.
```
  25.60
+ 32.47
  58.07 cm
      1
```

5. 15 000 + 22 000 = 37 000
   81 000 + 87 000 = 168 000
   103 000 + 98 000 = 201 000

   You should have circled:
   81 406 + 86 511 = 157 917

An Extra Challenge

1655   **1656**   **1657**
```
  643927       699748       908984
+  55821      +209236      + 71015
  699748       908984       979999
      1            1  1            1
```

Pages 8-9 — Subtraction

1.
```
  58698       66725       467894
− 31274      −51024      −242931
  27424       15701       224963
```

1.
```
  937861       8436       7268       641304
−  24581      −52.71     −49.64     −208172
  913280       31.65      23.04      433132
```

2.
```
  78.95
− 44.49
  34.46     So Zara has £34.46 left.
```

3. a)
```
  847612
− 315240
  532372
```
b)
```
  532372
−  16154
  516218
```

4.
```
  64332
− 45.28     So Jude's team ate 19.04 litres
  19.04     more than Keisha's.
```

5. a) 535 000 − 43 000 = 492 000
   b) Using rounding, the estimate is much bigger than their answer.

An Extra Challenge
```
  947260       486232       So 395 112
− 461028      −  91120      people went to see
  486232       395112       Goblins Forever.
```

Pages 10-11 — Factors and Multiples

1. a) 24 is a multiple of 4. ✔   b) 6 is a factor of 32. ✘
   c) 41 is a multiple of 3. ✘   d) 9 is a factor of 54. ✔
2. You should have circled cakes B, F and H.
3. a) 1, 56   4, 14   2, 28   7, 8
   b) 1, 63   3, 21   7, 9
4. Kevin is right. Common factors of 36 and 48: 1, 2, 3, 4, 6, 12.
5. a) 108, 117   b) 132, 144   c) 84, 90, 96   d) 91, 98, 105

An Extra Challenge

a) The prime numbers are 29, 31, 47 and 59.
b) 45, 57 and 81 share the common factors of 1 and 3.

Pages 12-13 — Multiplication

1. a) $7.4 \times 10 = 74$ b) $15 \times 100 = 1500$
   c) $1000 \times 82 = 82\,000$ d) $100 \times 9.33 = 933$
2. a)
```
   1280
 ×    3
   3840
      2
```
b)
```
   1095
 ×    5
   5475
     4 2
```
c)
```
   3412
 ×    6
  20472
     2 1
```

3. a)
```
     781
 ×    60
       0
   46860
   46860
```
b)
```
     991
 ×    14
    3964
    9910
   13874
       1
```
c)
```
     513
 ×    41
     513
   20520
   21033
       1
```

4. a) Farmer Wanda grew 29 952 carrots.
   b) 76 713 parrots live in the second rainforest.
```
   2304                3653
 ×   13              ×   21
   6912                3653
  23040               73060
  29952               76713
      1                   1
```

An Extra Challenge

$152 \times 43 = 6536$ $3293 \times 30 = 98\,790$
$7481 \times 7 = 52\,367$ $4503 \times 6 = 27\,018$

Answers

Pages 14-15 — Division

1.
$$3\overline{)9\ 0\ 3} = 3\ 0\ 1$$
$$8\overline{)1\ ^16\ 8} = 2\ 1$$
$$5\overline{)4\ ^44\ ^40} = 8\ 8$$

2. $2190 \div ? = 219 — 10$ $\qquad$ $68 \div ? = 6.8 — 10$
   $386 \div ? = 3.86 — 100$ $\qquad$ $702 \div ? = 0.702 — 1000$
   $4.3 \div ? = 0.43 — 10$ $\qquad$ $15.5 \div ? = 0.155 — 100$

3. $4\overline{)4\ 7\ ^37\ ^16} = 1\ 1\ 9\ 4$ $\qquad$ Each person made **1194** baubles.

4. $6\overline{)7\ ^13\ ^12\ 6} = 1\ 2\ 2\ 1$ $\qquad$ $1221 \div 100 = \textbf{12.21}$

5. a) $4\overline{)1\ ^14\ ^25\ ^19} = 3\ 6\ 4\ r\ 3$ $\qquad$ Each dolphin eats **364** fish and there are **3** left over.

   b) $7\overline{)5\ ^53\ ^44\ ^53\ ^3} = 7\ 6\ 4\ r\ 5$ $\qquad$ Each dolphin eats **764** fish and there are **5** left over.

An Extra Challenge

The original number was 20.9.
Dividing 2469 by 5 will leave a remainder of 4.
True — the answer to both calculations is 668.

Pages 16-17 — Fractions 1

1. Quentin $\longrightarrow \frac{1}{10}$ $\qquad$ Sofia $\longrightarrow \frac{3}{10}$ $\qquad$ Bogdan $\longrightarrow \frac{6}{10}$

2. $37\% = \frac{37}{100}$ $\qquad$ $0.86 = \frac{86}{100}$
   $54\% = \frac{54}{100}$ $\qquad$ $0.102 = \frac{102}{1000}$

3. $\square = \frac{6}{8}$ $\qquad$ $\square = \frac{3}{4}$ $\qquad$ $\square = \frac{12}{16}$

4. vanilla — $1\frac{4}{5}$ $\qquad$ strawberry — $1\frac{2}{3}$
   bubblegum — $2\frac{5}{11}$ $\qquad$ chocolate — $2\frac{3}{8}$

5. $\frac{24}{6} \longrightarrow \frac{26}{6}$ $\qquad$ $\frac{9}{2} \longrightarrow \frac{7}{2}$ $\qquad$ $\frac{33}{5} \longrightarrow \frac{39}{5}$

An Extra Challenge

The fractions Briony needs are $\frac{1}{3}$, $\frac{16}{24}$ and $\frac{5}{21}$.

Any suitable equivalent fractions. For example:

$\frac{1}{3} \longrightarrow \frac{2}{6}$ $\qquad$ $\frac{16}{24} \longrightarrow \frac{8}{12}$ $\qquad$ $\frac{5}{21} \longrightarrow \frac{10}{42}$

Pages 18-19 — Diving the Depths

1.
Depth (feet)	Rounded figure (nearest 1000)
11 820	12 000
15 468	15 000
19 157	19 000
23 913	24 000
27 176	27 000

2. -250 m $\qquad$ 500 m $\div 2 = 250$ m $\qquad$ $2\ °C \div 2 = 1\ °C$
   $\qquad\qquad\qquad$ $23\ °C - 1\ °C = \textbf{22 °C}$
   -2000 m $\qquad$ 2000 m $\div 500$ m $= 4$ $\qquad$ $2\ °C \times 4 = 8\ °C$
   $\qquad\qquad\qquad$ $23\ °C - 8\ °C = \textbf{15 °C}$
   -3500 m $\qquad$ 3500 m $\div 500$ m $= 7$ $\qquad$ $2\ °C \times 7 = 14\ °C$
   $\qquad\qquad\qquad$ $23\ °C - 14\ °C = \textbf{9 °C}$

3. $\frac{3}{5} = \frac{60}{100} = 60\%$ $\qquad$ $100\% - 60\% = 40\%$
   Yes, it was a prime number. $25 + 40 + 18 = 83$

4. 1 — 7776 ml $\qquad$ 2 — 16 425 ml $\qquad$ 3 — 14 015 ml

5. 1 km = 1000 m $\qquad$ $9.3 \times 1000 = \textbf{9300 m}$
   8700 m + 1400 m + 8700 m = 18 800 m = **18.8 km**

6. With the highlighted digits, the missing directions are 8 right, 4 down and 1 left, 3 down.

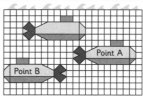

Pages 20-21 — Fractions 2

1. $\frac{7}{12} - \frac{2}{6} = \frac{7}{12} - \frac{4}{12} = \frac{3}{12}$ $\qquad$ $\frac{1}{2} + \frac{4}{14} = \frac{7}{14} + \frac{4}{14} = \frac{11}{14}$

2. $\frac{10}{18} — 3$ $\qquad$ $\frac{4}{9} — 2$ $\qquad$ $\frac{1}{6} — 1$ $\qquad$ $\frac{2}{3} — 4$

3. a) $\frac{4}{7}$ $\qquad$ b) $1\frac{4}{5}$ $\qquad$ c) $1\frac{4}{6} \left(\text{or } 1\frac{2}{3}\right)$ $\qquad$ d) $1\frac{2}{8} \left(\text{or } 1\frac{1}{4}\right)$

4. a) $1\frac{5}{12} - \frac{8}{12} = \frac{17}{12} - \frac{8}{12} = \frac{9}{12}$ $\qquad$ $\frac{1}{3} + \frac{3}{24} = \frac{8}{24} + \frac{3}{24} = \frac{11}{24}$
   $\frac{4}{16} + \frac{5}{8} = \frac{2}{8} + \frac{5}{8} = \frac{7}{8}$ $\qquad$ $\frac{13}{6} - 1\frac{1}{3} = \frac{13}{6} - \frac{8}{6} = \frac{5}{6}$
   b) $\frac{7}{8}$ $\qquad$ $\frac{5}{6}$ $\qquad$ $\frac{9}{12}$ $\qquad$ $\frac{11}{24}$

An Extra Challenge

$3 \times \frac{4}{5} = 2\frac{2}{5}$ $\qquad$ $4 \times 1\frac{1}{10} = 4\frac{4}{10}$ $\qquad$ $5 \times 1\frac{6}{15} = 7$

$2\frac{2}{5} + 4\frac{4}{10} + 7 = 13\frac{4}{5}$ bags of wool in total

Pages 22-23 — Converting Units

1. a) ✗ $\qquad$ b) ✔ $\qquad$ c) ✔ $\qquad$ d) ✗

2. mm to m $\div 1000$ $\qquad$ kg to g $\times 1000$ $\qquad$ cm to mm $\times 10$
   ml to l $\div 1000$ $\qquad$ cm to m $\div 100$

3. 2 days = 2×24 hours = 48 hours. $48 + 6 = 54$ hours, so Sonal's time is 54 hours 37 minutes. She beat her dad and her brother's times.

4. a) 4210 g = 4.21 kg $\qquad$ b) 15.5 litres = 15 500 ml
   c) 3860 m = 3.86 km $\qquad$ d) 17 cm = 0.17 m
   e) 2290 mm = 2.29 m $\qquad$ f) 10.52 kg = 10 520 g

5. South America: 98 days = $98 \div 7 = 14$ weeks
   Asia = 15 weeks $\qquad$ Africa: 63 days = $63 \div 7 = 9$ weeks
   Europe: $14 + 9 + 15 = 38$ weeks $\qquad$ $52 - 38 = 14$ weeks
   So Marek spent the most time in Asia.

An Extra Challenge

a) 2250 g = 2.25 kg $\qquad$ 1500 ml = 1.5 l $\qquad$ 0.52 kg = 520 g
   0.05 l = 50 ml $\qquad$ 0.03 kg = 30 g
b) 5 pounds ≈ 2.5 kg $\qquad$ 3 pints ≈ 1.5 l $\qquad$ 12 ounces ≈ 300 g
   1 pint ≈ 500 ml $\qquad$ 2 ounces ≈ 50 g
The chef can't make the tomato pasta because they don't have enough pasta.

Pages 24-25 — Problem Solving

1. Cola: 1.5 l = 1500 ml $\qquad$ Fizzy cherry: 2 l = 2000 ml
   Fizzy orange: 1.5 l = 1500 ml
   Total pop: 1500 + 2000 + 1500 = 5000 ml
   Total drunk: 670 + 1280 + 940 = 2890 ml
   Amount left: 5000 − 2890 = 2110 ml

2. a) $47 \times 325 = 15\ 275 = 15.275$ kg
   b) $\frac{1}{2} = 50\%$ $\qquad$ $20\% + 50\% = 70\%$
   $100\% - 70\% = 30\%$ $\qquad$ $30 \div 100 = \textbf{0.3}$

3. a) subscription: £1.50 $\qquad$ cards: £1.50 ÷ 2 = £0.75
   £1.50 + £0.75 = £2.25 $\qquad$ £2.25 × 10 weeks = **£22.50**

b) $\frac{1}{4}$ of his money: £22.50 ÷ 3 = **£7.50**

Starting amount: £22.50 + £7.50 = **£30.00**

An Extra Challenge

a) 1660 km × 4 = **6640 km**

b) 50% = $\frac{1}{2}$ $\frac{1}{2}$ of 1660 km = 1660 km ÷ 2 = **830 km**

c) $\frac{1}{10}$ of 1660 km = 1660 km ÷ 10 = 166 km

So Zia travels 1660 km + 166 km = **1826 km**

Pages 26-27 — Shapes and Angles

1. A — 140°   B — 15°   C — 95°   D — 200°

2.

3. a = **8 cm**   b = 90° − 35° = **55°**
    c = 90° − 71° = **19°**   d = **3 cm**

4. = 115°   = 68°

5. Crocodile: The mouth is a right angle, so the angles add up to 90°.   40° + 32° = 72°   90° − 72° = **18°**
    Snake: Its body makes one whole turn, so all the angles add up to 360°.   90° + 90° + 67° = 247°   360° − 247° = **113°**
    Giraffe: Its neck is a straight line, so all the angles add up to 180°.   41° + 29° + 52° = 122°   180° − 122° = **58°**

An Extra Challenge

Group 1: regular shapes — heptagon and pentagon
Group 2: irregular shapes with angles of 90° or less
            — isosceles triangle and rectangle
Group 3: irregular shapes with reflex angles — heart

Pages 28-29 — Perimeter and Area

1. Garden 1 — **56 m**   a = 8 − 4 = 4 m   b = 20 − 12 = 8 m
    Garden 2 — **30 m**   c = 2 m   d = 5 m
    Garden 3 — **42 m**   e: 4.5 + 4.5 = 9   9 − 3 = 6 m
                           f: 6 + 6 = 12   12 − 3 = 9 m

2. Seal: 5 m²   Castle: 7 m²   For sale sign: 7 × 11 = 77 cm²
    Meal deal sign: 9 × 9 = 81 cm²

3. Top left shell: 4 cm²   Top right shell: 5 cm²
    Bottom left shell: 3 cm²   Bottom right shell: 2 cm²

4. a) 10 cm   b) 15 cm   c) 14 cm

5. a) width = **2 cm**   14 − 5 − 5 = 4 cm   4 ÷ 2 = 2 cm
    b) length = **9 cm**   26 − 4 − 4 = 18 cm   18 ÷ 2 = 9 cm
    c) width = **3.5 cm**   31 − 12 − 12 = 7 cm   7 ÷ 2 = 3.5 cm
    d) perimeter = **29 cm**   6.5 + 6.5 = 13 cm
                          8 + 8 = 16 cm   13 + 16 = 29 cm

An Extra Challenge

24 squares are more than half covered by dough, and 10 squares are more than half covered by bear shapes. So the estimated area of dough left once the shapes are cut out is 24 − 10 = 14 cm².

Pages 30-31 — 3D Shapes

1. a) 7 cm³   b) 10 cm³   c) 9 cm³

2.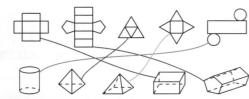

3. a) Bag A: 18 cm³   Bag B: 12 cm³   Bag C: 21 cm³
    b) sweet = 4 cm³   keyring = 7 cm³   orange = 8 cm³
    phone = 6 cm³   So Bag A will hold the sweet, orange and phone, Bag B will hold the sweet and orange, and Bag C will hold the keyring, orange and phone.

An Extra Challenge

a)   b)
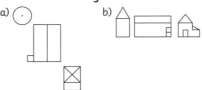

Pages 32-33 — Reflection and Translation

1. a)
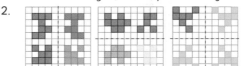

    ✗   ✓   ✗

    b) In the first grid, the shape has changed shape.
    In the third grid, the shape has changed size.

2.

3. red: 2 left, 4 down   orange: 5 right, 1 up
    blue: 3 right, 2 down   yellow: 5 left, 5 up

4.

An Extra Challenge

Pages 34-35 — Graphs and Tables

1.

	Total races	Total wins
Speedy Susan	38	34
Slimy Shelly	35	26
Steve T Snail	42	39
Sally Slowpoke	29	17

2. a) True. 45 minutes = 15 mm   90 minutes = 40 mm
    40 mm − 15 mm = 25 mm
    b) False. 60 minutes = 20 mm   120 minutes = 55 mm
    55 mm − 20 mm = 35 mm

3. a) 35 minutes
    b) Parade 1: 43 minutes   Parade 2: 51 minutes
    Parade 3: 47 minutes   So Parade 2 will last the longest.
    c) year 3 = 500 people   year 8 = 1750 people
    1750 − 500 = **1250 fewer people**
    year 2 = 250 people   year 5 = 2250 people
    2250 − 250 = 2000   2000 ÷ 2 = 1000
    In year 10, there are 250 + 1000 = **1250 people**.

An Extra Challenge

Item	Total ordered
Fabric squares	340
Balls of wool	252
Beads	1350
Coloured threads	428